Best in Children's Books

Noah's Ark

retold and illustrated
by TONY PALAZZO

There was a storm a long time ago. The story of Noah is the story of that storm. It almost destroyed the earth we live in and the people in it.

There have been many kinds of storms since the world first began . . .

HURRICANES——that carry houses away.

TORNADOES——that uproot trees.

And TYPHOONS——that toss ships about!

2

Yet there once was a storm that was more terrible than any
of these.

It was more than a storm. It was a flood that covered the
whole world.

It was more than a flood. It was a *deluge!*

There was only one boat left in the world. It was built by a
man and his three sons.

3

The man was Noah.

The boat was called Noah's Ark.

The Ark was built so that all the animals could be saved as well as Noah's family.

This great storm happened before raincoats. It happened before silk umbrellas. It happened even before rubbers!

It was a very long time ago.
And Noah alone received the news of the storm.

There would be water everywhere and it would cover the earth completely. There would be no land anywhere, not even a beach to stand on or a path to walk along.

Noah was told all this by God Himself shortly before it happened.

I'll build a boat, Noah thought.

No, I had better build a ship, he said to himself.

His warning came from God Himself!

There would be rain.

LOTS OF RAIN.

It would pour. And the heavens would open up!

The big rains would begin soon and would not stop for forty days and forty nights.

And there would be a flood and all the living creatures remaining on earth would perish!

A BIG FLOOD...
bigger than a puddle.

Bigger than a rain barrel.

Even bigger than a swimming pool!

5

he was commanded by God.

God's voice sounded like thunder:

Build it tall and wide and waterproof. Build it three stories high and two houses wide. Have a door on the ground floor and a window on the top floor. Have rooms in it for yourself and your wife—for your sons and their wives—

7

and for some of each of all the living creatures of the earth.

In the Ark, take at least one male and one female of all the creatures that walk the earth,

and all that crawl...

and all that fly.

And take food. Take food for you, and food for your family, and food for all the creatures. Take enough food to last the whole time of the flood that will follow the rain.

Noah was fortunate that he received all this good advice from God. And he set to work.

With only a short time in which to build the Ark, Noah was a busy man, and so were his sons.

Yet, soon it was *finished*, and ready to receive the animals. The food was stored in the huge bins.

Seven days before the rains started the animals began the long walk up into the Ark.

Two by two they came.

Elephant bull and elephant cow,

A stallion and a mare,

A ram, a ewe,

And squirrels, too,

The tortoise and the hare.

A rooster and a cackling hen,

A gander and a goose,

A turkey tom, and a turkey hen,

Two monkeys, and two moose.

On they came from near and far,
the creatures of the earth.

Two by two, from near and far,
They made the Ark their berth.

They crawled.

They crept,

And some high-stepped
Along the jungle road.

They waddled,

And they galloped, too, to reach the dry abode.

Every living thing, every beast, those with four feet and those with two feet.

Every crawling, creeping creature,

all the birds that fly,

and all the birds that do not fly.

They all came to Noah's Ark.

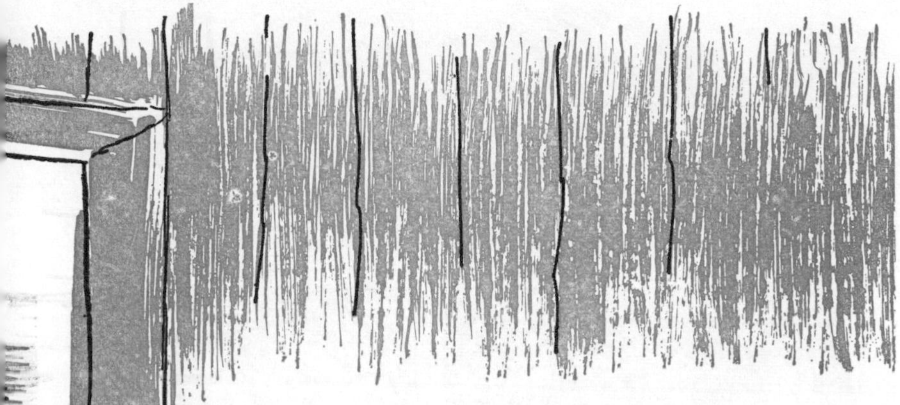

Two by two the male and female of each kind were met by Noah and told where their space was in the great Ark.

Then there came a time after many hours when all were inside.
And the sky was dark and angry with gathering rain clouds.

And the great door on the ground floor was shut tight, and the window on the top floor was closed.

And the rains began.

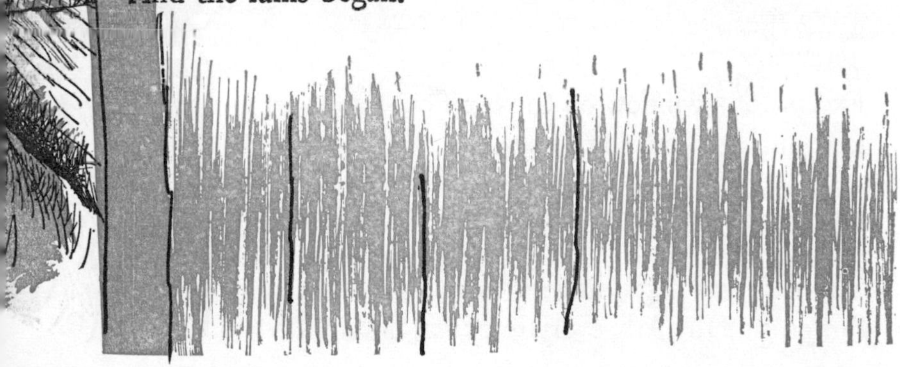

Except for a window on the top floor there was nowhere to look out, and nothing to see.

But the rain rattled on the roof, and that could be *heard*.

The Ark was beginning to float, and that could be *felt*. But outside the Ark, everything was different!

24

Everything wasn't there anymore!

Except water, rain, and sky.

Not a tree, not a house, not even a chimney-top!

and it rained...

and rained...

AND RAINED!

Finally, just as God had told Noah it would happen, the rains stopped on the fortieth night of the fortieth day.

And the pitter-patter on the roof stopped, though the Ark continued to float. Noah went up to the top-floor window to see what he could see.

But he could see no land close by, and sent forth a raven to fly over the water and find dry land.

The bird flew out of the window never to return.

Then after some days Noah sent forth a dove.

And the dove soon returned, for there was no dry place to set her feet or rest her tired wings.

Yet the next time she flew forth she quickly returned with a green olive leaf in her beak.

And Noah knew by this sign that the flood had passed and that somewhere there was dry land.

He opened the door on the first floor

to let the setting sun bathe the Ark.

It was then that Noah discovered the mighty Ark had come to rest high on a mountaintop.

Then God spoke to him again:

You may leave the Ark now, Noah, and let all the living creatures within leave the Ark, that they may multiply and inhabit the earth.

And all the creatures then came out of the Ark in the same manner as they had entered it.

They climbed down the mountaintop, clambered down the rocks, and scattered through the hills.

They romped happily into a sunlit world they had not seen for many, many days.

They made a joyful procession as they left the Ark.

The chittering monkeys

and the ponderous elephants.

The gay zebras

and the solemn turtles.

The soft, warm cats

and the cold, crawling snakes.

The tall giraffes and the low-slung hippos.

It was like the beginning of a new world, and as Noah looked toward the sky he saw a great rainbow.

God said: *Look now, upon that rainbow and know that for all time it will follow the rain. It is My promise that there shall never again be a flood to destroy the world.*

And thus it is, even today.

Pocahontas

illustrated by VLADIMIR BOBRI

Once upon a time, when America was a wilderness, a little Indian Princess called Pocahontas lived in the country that is now Virginia, in the longhouse of her father, great Chief Powhatan.

Everyone in all the thirty tribes that Powhatan ruled feared the stern chief — everyone except Pocahontas! The pretty child was her father's pet. He gave her whatever she wanted, for he could not resist her bright, brave, happy ways.

Powhatan was a strong ruler in a land of peace and plenty.

Then, one warm spring day, the white men came.

In enormous ships they sailed up the river, and began to cut down the giant trees, and make themselves a town.

39

When Powhatan saw how these pale-faced strangers destroyed his wild forest, and hunted down his deer and turkeys, he was very angry; and he made up his mind that they must all be killed.

He sent his best braves, armed with bows and arrows and tomahawks, into the white men's town. But the white men had magic on their side. They pointed sticks that, with a loud roar, shot fire and lead among the Indians. Dozens of the braves were killed, and the rest ran back into the protection of the forest.

So, many moons went by and still the white men stayed on in Powhatan's land.

Then, one day in early autumn, some Indians captured a white man who was hunting alone in the woods. They bound his arms with deer sinews, and carried him to Powhatan. The Chief at once decided that this pale-faced prisoner must die.

All the wise men and the medicine men and the women and the children of Powhatan's village gathered in a circle around the great, flat stone where the white man was to be executed. Many of them were afraid, for they knew the white man's magic and they wondered what this one might yet do.

But Pocahontas, who stood beside her father, was not afraid. She saw with surprise the man's pale skin, light hair, and bright blue eyes. She saw how bravely and quietly he stood, and she pitied him, for she thought he looked wise and kind.

And, indeed, Pocahontas had discovered the truth. This man was Captain John Smith, brave leader of the little English colony, who had wished only to make friends with the Indians.

Now Captain Smith was led to the stone, was made to kneel and place his head upon it. Two tall Indian braves with war clubs in their hands came forward. The chief and his people waited breathless. The Indian braves raised their mighty clubs.

Suddenly, from the circle of watchers darted the small figure of Pocahontas. She threw herself between Captain Smith and the uplifted clubs. She threw her arms around him and laid her head on his.

"Father," she cried, "spare this man's life. Surely he has done us no evil. He will be our friend."

The men with the clubs dared not strike lest they hurt the little Princess. A great cry arose from the people, and Powhatan ordered his daughter back to his side.

Pocahontas did not move. Fixing her beautiful eyes on her father's face, she pleaded for the prisoner's life.

At last, Powhatan gave the order that the white man was to be set free. The great Chief could never deny his lovely child anything she asked for. And she had asked for the life of Captain John Smith.

After that, for as long as she lived, Pocahontas was a friend of the white men. She helped them in time of famine by bringing them corn and deer meat. She warned Captain Smith, time and again, when her father's tribes made plans to murder all the settlers in the tiny Jamestown colony. When she grew up, she joined the English church, was christened Rebecca, and married a young settler named John Rolfe.

Then, one day, with her husband and her baby son, she sailed to England. There, in the homes of lords and ladies and in the very palace of the King, she was received as "Lady Rebecca" and "Princess Pocahontas."

She never returned to Virginia, but her son did. And many Americans today are proud to claim this brave Indian girl as one of their ancestors.

The Fisherman and His Wife

by JAKOB *and* WILHELM GRIMM

illustrated by ROBIN JACQUES

There was once a fisherman and his wife who lived together in a hovel by the seashore; and the fisherman went out every day, and he fished, and he fished.

One day when he was sitting and looking into the clear water, down went the line to the bottom, and when he drew it up he found a great flounder on the hook. And the flounder said to him, "Fisherman, listen to me; let me go. I am not a real fish but an enchanted prince. What use shall I be to you if you land me? I shall not taste good. Put me back into the sea again, and let me swim away."

"Well," said the fisherman, "no need for so many words about the matter. I had much rather let a talking fish go, than keep him."

Then he put him back into the clear water, and the flounder sank to the bottom, leaving a long streak of blood behind him. Then the fisherman got up and went home to his wife in their hovel.

"Well, husband," said the wife, "have you caught nothing today?"

"No," said the man. "I did catch a flounder, but as he said he was an enchanted prince, I let him go again."

"But, didn't you wish for anything?" asked the wife.

"No," said the man. "What should I wish for?"

"Oh, dear!" said the wife. "It is so dreadful always to live in this evil-smelling hovel; you might have wished for a little cottage. Go again and call him; tell him we want a little cottage. I daresay he will give it us; go, and be quick."

When he went back, the sea was green and yellow, and not nearly so clear. But he stood and said,

> "O man, O man!—if man you be,
> Or flounder, flounder, in the sea—
> Such a tiresome wife I've got,
> For she wants what I do not."

Then the flounder came swimming up, and said, "Now then, what does she want?"

"Oh," said the man, "my wife says I ought to have wished for something before I let you go. She does not want to live any longer in the hovel, and would rather have a cottage."

"Go home with you," said the flounder. "She has it already."

So the man went home, and found, instead of the hovel, a little cottage, and his wife was sitting on a bench before

46

the door. And she took him by the hand, and said to him, "Come in and see if this is not a great improvement."

So they went in, and there was a little parlor and a beautiful little bedroom, a kitchen and larder, with all sorts of furniture and pots and pans and dishes of the very best. And at the back was a little yard with fowls and ducks, and a little garden full of green vegetables and fruit.

47

"Look," said the wife. "Is not this nice?"

"Yes," said the man, "we shall be very well contented."

"We will see about that," said the wife. And after a meal they went to bed.

So all went well for a week or two; then the wife said, "Look here, husband, the cottage is really too small, and the yard and garden are so tiny. I think the flounder had better get us a larger house; so go to your fish and ask for a big stone castle."

"O my dear wife," said the man, "the cottage is good enough; what do we want a castle for?"

"We want one," said the wife. "Go along with you; the flounder can give us one."

"Now, wife," said the man, "the flounder gave us the cottage. I do not like to go to him again; he may be angry."

"Go along," said the wife, "he might just as well give it to us as not. Do as I say!"

The man felt very reluctant; and he said to himself, "It is not the right thing to do." Nevertheless he went.

When he came to the seaside, the water was dark purple and grey and thick, and not green and yellow as before. And he stood and said,

> *"O man, O man!—if man you be,*
> *Or flounder, flounder, in the sea—*
> *Such a tiresome wife I've got,*
> *For she wants what I do not."*

"Now then, what does she want?" said the flounder.

"Oh," said the man, half frightened, "she wants to live in a big stone castle."

"Go home with you; she is already standing before the door," said the flounder.

Then the man went home, and there, in place of the cottage, stood a great castle of stone. His wife was standing on the steps, about to go in; so she took him by the hand, and said, "Let us enter."

With that he went in with her; and in the castle was a great hall with a marble pavement; and there were many servants who led them through large doors; and the passages were decked with tapestry, and the rooms with golden chairs and tables, and crystal chandeliers hanging from the ceiling; and all the rooms had carpets. And the tables were covered with the best food and wines. And at the back of the house was a great courtyard with stables for horses, cattle, and carriages of the finest. Besides, there was a splendid large garden, with the most beautiful flowers and fine fruit trees, and a park full half a mile long, with deer and oxen and sheep, and everything that the heart could wish for.

"There!" said the wife. "Is not this beautiful?"

"Oh yes," said the man. "We can live in this fine castle and be very well contented."

"We will see about that," said the wife; and they went to bed.

The next morning the wife was awake first, just at the break of day, and she looked out and saw from her bed the beautiful country lying all around. She poked the man in the side with her elbow, and said, "Husband, just think if we could be King over all this country. Go to your fish and tell him we should like to be King."

"Now, wife," said the man, "what should we be King for? I don't want to be King."

"Well," said the wife, "if you don't want to be King, I will be King."

"Now, wife," said the man, "I could not ask him such a thing."

"Why not?" said the wife. "Go directly; I must be King."

So the man went, thinking, "It is not the right thing to do—not at all the right thing."

And when he came to the sea the water was quite dark grey, and rushed far inland, and had an evil smell. And he stood and said,

> *"O man, O man!—if man you be,*
> *Or flounder, flounder, in the sea—*
> *Such a tiresome wife I've got,*
> *For she wants what I do not."*

"Now then, what does she want?" said the fish.

"Oh, dear!" said the man. "She wants to be King."

"Go home with you; she is so already," said the fish.

So the man went back, and as he came to the palace he saw it was very much larger, and had great towers and splendid gateways. A herald stood before the door, and a number of soldiers with kettledrums and trumpets.

And when he came inside everything was of marble and gold, and there were many curtains with great golden tassels. Then he went through the doors of the great throne room, and there was his wife sitting upon a throne of gold and diamonds, and she had a great golden crown on, and the sceptre in her hand was of pure gold and jewels, and on

52

each side stood six pages in a row, each one a head shorter than the other. So the man went up to her and said, "Well, wife, so now you are King!"

"Yes," said the wife, "now I am King."

So then he stood and looked at her, and when he had gazed at her for some time he said, "Well, wife, this is fine for you to be King! Now there is nothing more to wish for."

"O husband!" said the wife, seeming quite restless, "I am tired of this already. Go to your fish and tell him that now I am King I must be Emperor."

"Now, wife," said the man, "what do you want to be Emperor for?"

"Husband," said she, "go and tell the fish I want to be Emperor."

"Oh dear!" said the man. "He could not do it—I cannot ask him such a thing. There is but one Emperor at a time; the fish can't possibly make anyone Emperor—indeed he can't."

"Now, look here," said the wife, "I am King, and you are only my husband, so will you go at once? If he was able to make me King, he is able to make me Emperor; and I will and must be Emperor, so go along!"

So he was obliged to go; and as he went he felt very uncomfortable about it, and he thought to himself, "It is not at all the right thing to do; to want to be Emperor is really going too far; the flounder will soon begin to get tired of this."

With that he came to the sea, and the water was quite black and thick, and the foam flew, and the wind blew, and the man was terrified. But he stood and said,

> "O man, O man!—if man you be,
> Or flounder, flounder, in the sea—
> Such a tiresome wife I've got,
> For she wants what I do not."

"What is it now?" said the fish.

"Oh dear!" said the man, "my wife wants to be Emperor."

"Go home with you," said the fish. "She is Emperor already."

So the man went home, and found the castle adorned with polished marble and alabaster figures, and golden gates. The troops were being marshalled before the door, and they were blowing trumpets and beating drums and cymbals; and when he entered he saw barons and earls and dukes waiting about like servants; and the doors were of bright gold. And he saw his wife sitting upon a throne made of one entire piece of gold, and it was about two miles high; and she had a great golden crown on, which was about three yards high, set with diamonds and rubies; and in one hand she held the sceptre, and in the other the globe; and on both sides of her stood pages in two rows, all

arranged according to their size, from the most enormous
giant of two miles high to the tiniest dwarf of the size of
my little finger; and before her stood earls and dukes in
crowds. So the man went up to her and said, "Well, wife,
so now you are Emperor."

"Yes," said she, "now I am Emperor."

Then he went and sat down and had a good look at her,
and then he said, "Well now, wife, there is nothing left to
be, now you are Emperor."

"What are you talking about, husband?" said she. "I am Emperor, and next I will be Pope! So go and tell the fish so."

"Oh dear!" said the man, "what is it that you don't want? You can never become Pope; there is but one Pope in Christendom, and the fish can't possibly do it."

"Husband," said she, "no more words about it. I must and will be Pope; so go along to the fish."

"Now, wife," said the man, "how can I ask him such a thing? It is too bad—it is asking a little too much."

"What rubbish!" said the wife. "If he could make me Emperor, he can make me Pope. Go along and ask him; I am Emperor, and you are only my husband, so go you must."

So he went, feeling very frightened, and he shivered and shook, and his knees trembled; and there arose a great wind, and the clouds flew by, and it grew very dark, and the sea rose mountains high, and the ships were tossed about,

and the sky was partly blue in the middle, but at the sides very dark and red, as in a great tempest. And he felt very desponding, and stood trembling and said,

> *"O man, O man!—if man you be,*
> *Or flounder, flounder, in the sea—*
> *Such a tiresome wife I've got,*
> *For she wants what I do not."*

"Well, what now?" said the fish.

"Oh dear!" said the man. "She wants to be Pope."

"Go home with you; she is Pope already," said the fish.

So he went home, and he found himself before a great church, with palaces all around. He had to make his way through a crowd of people; and when he got inside he

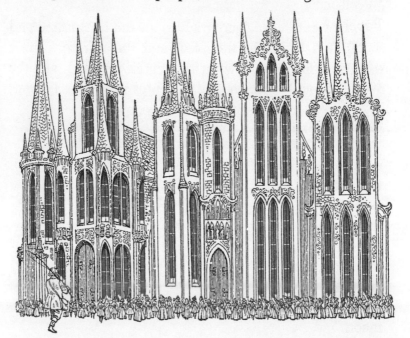

found the place lighted up with thousands and thousands of lights; and his wife was clothed in a golden garment, and sat upon a very high throne, and had three golden crowns on, all in the greatest priestly pomp; and on both sides of her there stood two rows of lighted candles—from the tallest, as big as a tower, to the smallest, a tiny rushlight; and all the emperors and kings were kneeling before her and kissing her foot.

"Well, wife," said the man, and sat and stared at her, "so you are Pope."

"Yes," said she, "now I am Pope!"

And he went on gazing at her till he felt dazzled, as if he were sitting in the sun. And after a little time he said, "Well, now, wife, what is there left to be, now you are Pope?"

And she sat up very stiff and straight, and said nothing.

And he said again, "Well, wife, I hope you are contented at last with being Pope; you can be nothing more."

"We will see about that," said the wife, and with that they both went to bed.

The husband slept soundly after his busy day; but the wife tossed and turned from side to side the whole night through, thinking all the while what she could be next, but nothing occurred to her. And when she saw the red dawn she slipped off the bed, and sat before the window to see the sun rise, and as it came up she said, "Ah, I have it! What if I could make the sun and moon to rise—husband!" she cried, and stuck her elbow in his ribs. "Wake up, and go to your fish, and tell him I want power over the sun and moon."

The man was so fast asleep that when he started up he fell out of bed. Then he shook himself together, and opened his eyes and said, "Oh—wife, what did you say?"

"Husband," said she, "if I cannot be like God and make the sun and moon rise when I want them, I shall never have another quiet hour. Go to the fish and tell him so."

"O wife!" said the man, and fell on his knees to her. "The fish can really not do that for you. I grant you he could make you Emperor and Pope; do be contented with that, I beg of you."

But she became wild with impatience, and screamed out, "I can wait no longer; go at once!"

And so off he went as well as he could, for a dreadful storm was rising and he could hardly keep his feet. Houses and trees were blown down; the mountains trembled, and rocks fell into the sea. The sky was quite black, and it thundered and lightened; and the waves, crowned with foam, ran mountains high. So he cried out, without being able to hear his own words,

> "O man, O man!—if man you be,
> Or flounder, flounder, in the sea—
> Such a tiresome wife I've got,
> For she wants what I do not."

"Well, what now?" said the flounder.

"Oh dear!" said the man. "She wants to be like God and order the sun and moon."

"Go home with you!" said the flounder. "You will find her in the old hovel."

And there they are sitting to this very day.

Mrs. Piggle-Wiggle's Won't-Pick-Up-Toys Cure

by BETTY MACDONALD

illustrated by BURMAH BURRIS

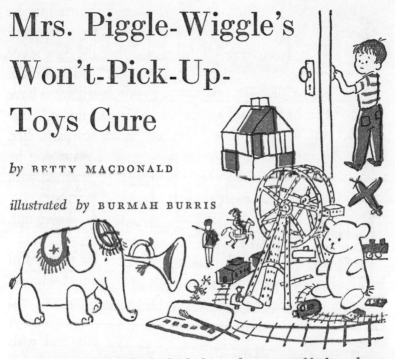

Hubert was a very lucky little boy whose grandfather always sent him wonderful toys for Christmas. Hubert's mother said that his grandfather sent him these marvelous presents because Hubert was such a dear little boy. His father said that it was to make up for that awful name they had wished on him. Hubert was named for his grandfather. His full name was Hubert Egbert Prentiss.

Hubert liked the presents his grandfather sent him, but who wouldn't? He had an electric train with track that went four times around his bedroom and into the closet and out again and had seven stations and every signal there

was and two bridges and a snow shed. He also had a Little-Builder set so large that he could build regular office

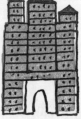

buildings; and a great big wagon full of stone blocks made into shapes so that he could build big stone bridges for his electric train and stone buildings and even stone barracks

for his one thousand and five hundred toy soldiers. Hubert

also had a circus with every kind of wooden, jointed animal and clowns and tightrope walkers and trapeze artists. He had a little typewriter, and a real desk and a little radio and two automobiles. He had about a hundred or more air-

planes and little cars. He had a fire engine with real sirens

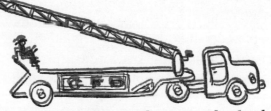

and lights and hook and ladders; and so many books that he had to have two bookcases in his room.

Hubert liked all of his toys and he was moderately generous about letting other children play with them, but he never put his things away. When his mother made his bed she had to pick her way around and in and out and over the electric train and track. She had to take circus performers off the bureau and the bed posts. She had to pick up books that had been thrown face down on the floor and she was continually gathering up the Little-Builder set. It used to take her about three hours to do Hubert's room and about one hour to do the rest of her housework.

She would send Hubert up to put his toys away, but all he ever did was to stuff them under the bed or into the closet and in the morning when his mother cleaned his room, there they were for her to pick up.

Mrs. Prentiss was getting a little bored with this.

One rainy Saturday Hubert invited all of his little friends to play up in his room. He had Dicky and Charlie and Billy and Tommy and Bobby. They got out every single toy that Hubert owned and played with them and then, just before dinner, they all went home and left the mess. Hubert's mother didn't know a thing about this until the next morning when she went in to make Hubert's bed. Then she just stood in the doorway and looked. The electric train track went under the bed five times and under the bureau and under the chairs and around the desk and into the closet. All along the track were bridges and buildings of the stone blocks and whole towns built from the Little-Builder

set. On the bed and under the bed and on the bureau were the circus tent, the animals, the clowns, the tightrope walkers and the trapeze artists. The floor was littered with books and little automobiles and airplanes and painting sets and chemical sets and woodburning sets and crayons and coloring books and the little typewriter and the printing set and teddy bears and balls and jacks and parchesi games and jigsaw puzzles and soldiers, soldiers, soldiers.

Perspiration broke out on Hubert's mother's forehead and she began to feel faint, so she closed the door and slowly went downstairs.

She took two aspirin tablets and then telephoned her friend, Mrs. Bags. She said, "Hello, Mrs. Bags, this is Hubert's mother and I am so disappointed in Hubert. He has such lovely toys—his grandfather sends them to him every Christmas, you know—but he does not take care of them at all. He just leaves them all over his room for me to pick up every morning."

Mrs. Bags said, "Well, I'm sorry, Mrs. Prentiss, but I can't help you because you see, I think it is too late."

"Why, it's only nine-thirty," said Hubert's mother.

"Oh, I mean late in life," said Mrs. Bags. "You see, we started Ermintrude picking up her toys when she was six months old. 'A place for everything and everything in its place,' we have always told Ermintrude. Now, she is so neat that she becomes hysterical if she sees a crumb on the floor."

"Well, I certainly hope she never sees Hubert's room," said Mrs. Prentiss dryly. "She'd probably have a fit." And she hung up the phone.

Then she called Mrs. Moohead. "Good morning, Mrs. Moohead," she said. "Does Gregory pick up his toys?"

"Well, no, he doesn't," said Mrs. Moohead. "But you know Gregory is rather delicate and I feel that just playing with his toys tires him so much that I personally see that all of his little friends put the toys away before they go home."

"That is a splendid idea," said Hubert's mother, "but I am trying to train Hubert, not his playmates."

"Well, of course, Hubert is very strong and healthy, but Gregory is intelligent," said Mrs. Moohead.

"Is he?" said Mrs. Prentiss crossly, because she resented this inference that her son was all brawn and no brain.

"Oh, dear," squealed Mrs. Moohead, "I think Gregory is running a temperature. I must go to him." She hung up the phone.

Mrs. Prentiss then called Mrs. Grapple. "Hello, Marge," she said. "How's Susan?"

Mrs. Grapple said, "I've spanked her seven times since

66

breakfast and I just heard a crash so she is probably getting ready for another. How's Hubert?"

"That's what I called about," said Mrs. Prentiss. "Can you suggest a way to make Hubert *want* to pick up his toys? His room looks like a toy store after an earthquake."

"Why don't you call this Mrs. Piggle-Wiggle? I have heard she is perfectly wonderful. All the children in town adore her and she has a cure for everything. As soon as I spank Susan, I'm going to call her."

Hubert's mother said, "Thank you very much, Marge. That is just what I'll do. I had forgotten about Mrs. Piggle-Wiggle, but I just know she can help me."

So she called Mrs. Piggle-Wiggle and said, "Mrs. Piggle-Wiggle, I hate to bother you, but you seem always to know what to do about children and I'll confess that I don't know what to do to make Hubert put his toys away."

Mrs. Piggle-Wiggle said, "Hubert is the sweet little boy with all the wonderful toys that his grandfather sends him, isn't he?"

Mrs. Prentiss said, "Why, yes, but I didn't know that you knew him."

"Oh, yes," said Mrs. Piggle-Wiggle, "Hubert and I are old friends. In fact, he is building an automobile in my

back yard out of orange crates and empty tomato cans. Hubert is a very good carpenter."

Hubert's mother thought of the two little automobiles with rubber tires, real horns, leather seats big enough for two boys and lights that turned on with a switch, that Hubert's grandfather had given him; and she wondered why in the world he would want to build an automobile out of old orange crates and tomato cans. She said, however, "So that is where he and Dicky go every afternoon. I certainly hope he behaves himself."

"Oh, he does," said Mrs. Piggle-Wiggle. "We are all very fond of Hubert. But this problem of his toys. Let me see." Mrs. Piggle-Wiggle was quiet for some time. Then she said, "I think that the best thing for you to use is my old-fashioned Won't-Pick-Up-Toys cure. Starting now, don't pick up any of Hubert's toys. Don't make his bed. In fact, do not go into his room. When his room becomes so messy he can't get out of it, call me." Mrs. Piggle-Wiggle said goodbye and hung up the phone.

Hubert's mother, looking very relieved, went gaily about her housework, baked a chocolate cake for dinner, and did not say a word to Hubert when he came home with ten little boys and they all trailed upstairs to play in Hubert's room.

The next morning when Hubert came downstairs for breakfast his mother noticed that he had a little pan of water-color paint stuck in his hair and his shirt had purple ink from the printing set on one shoulder. She said nothing, but tripped upstairs after breakfast and quickly shut the door of his room.

The next morning Hubert's mother had a little trouble shutting the door of his room, and she noticed that Hubert had circles under his eyes as though he had not slept very well.

The next morning Hubert was very late coming downstairs and before he opened his door his mother heard a great clatter and scraping as though he were moving furniture. He had Little-Builder bolts stuck to his sweater and two paint pans in his hair. He was so sleepy he could barely keep his eyes open and he had a red mark on one cheek. His mother looked at it closely and saw that it was the shape and size of one of his stone blocks. He must have slept with his head on one of the bridges.

On the seventh day after Hubert's mother stopped putting away his toys, he did not come down to breakfast at all. About eleven o'clock his mother became worried and called up Mrs. Piggle-Wiggle.

She said, "Good morning, Mrs. Piggle-Wiggle. This is the seventh day of the old-fashioned Won't-Pick-Up-Toys cure and I am worried. Hubert has not come downstairs at all this morning."

Mrs. Piggle-Wiggle said, "Let me see! The seventh day —it usually takes ten days—but Hubert has so many toys he would naturally be quicker."

"Quicker at what?" asked Hubert's mother anxiously.

"Quicker at getting trapped in his room," said Mrs. Piggle-Wiggle. "You see, the reason Hubert hasn't come downstairs is that he cannot get out of his room. Have you noticed anything different about him lately?"

"Well," said Hubert's mother, "he looks as though he hadn't been sleeping well and on the fourth morning he had a red blotch on his cheek just the shape of one of his stone blocks."

"Hmmmmm," said Mrs. Piggle-Wiggle. "He probably can't get at his bed and is sleeping with his head on his blocks for a pillow."

"But what will I do?" asked Hubert's mother. "How will I feed him?"

"Wait until he calls for food, then tell him to open the

window and you put a piece of rather dry bread and peanut butter on the garden rake. He will have to drink out of the hose. Tie it to the rake and poke it up to him."

When Hubert's mother hung up the telephone she heard a muffled shouting from the direction of Hubert's room. She hurried upstairs and listened outside the door. Hubert was shouting, "Mother, I'm hungry!"

His mother said, "Go over and open the window, dear. I

will send something up to you on the rake."

Mrs. Prentiss took the crusty piece of a very old loaf of bread, spread some peanut butter on it, and took it around to the side of the house. Pretty soon Hubert's window was raised about a foot, and a hand and arm appeared. His mother stuck the bread on one of the tines of the rake and poked it up at the window. The hand groped around for a while and then found the bread and jerked it off. The window banged shut.

That night when Hubert's father came home his mother told him all about Mrs. Piggle-Wiggle's treatment. Hubert's father said, "Mrs. Piggle-Wiggle sounds all right, but none of this would have happened if Hubert's grandfather hadn't given him so many toys. When I was a boy all I needed to have a good time was a little piece of string and a stick. Why, I—"

Mrs. Prentiss said, "Not that old string-and-stick routine again, John. Anyway now that Hubert has the toys the picture is changed."

Mr. Prentiss hid his face behind the evening paper and said, "Something smells delicious. Is it Irish stew, I hope?"

"Yes, dear," said Hubert's mother, worrying about how she was going to serve Irish stew to Hubert on a rake. She finally put a potato on one prong, a carrot on another, an onion on another, and pieces of meat on the last three. The window was opened only about three inches, but the hand grabbed the food. After dinner Hubert's father tied the hose to the rake and held it up while Hubert put his mouth to the window opening and tried to get a drink of water. It was not very successful, but he managed to get a few drops.

Mrs. Prentiss was worried. The next morning she knocked on Hubert's door and said, "Hubert, what are you doing in there?"

Hubert said, "I've got a bear pen made out of bureau drawers and my bed's the mother bear's house and my train runs under my bed thirteen times now."

"Hubert, dear, don't you think you should try and come out soon?" asked his mother.

Hubert said, "I don't wanna come out. I like it in here. All my toys are out and I can play with them any old time I wanna. This is fun."

His mother went downstairs and called Mrs. Piggle-Wiggle. Mrs. Piggle-Wiggle said, "Oh, but he will want to come out. Wait and see."

That afternoon about two o'clock there was music on the street and children's voices laughing and calling and

pretty soon, right past Hubert's house, marched Mrs. Piggle-Wiggle and all the children and right behind them came the circus parade. Hubert managed, by putting one foot in a bureau drawer and the other in a freight car of his train, to get up to the window and look out. He waved to Mrs. Piggle-Wiggle and she called, "Hurry, hurry, Hubert! We are going to march all over town and then we are all going to the circus."

Hubert turned around quickly with the idea of getting to the door and joining the fun, but the freight car went scooting under the bed and the bureau drawer tipped over

73

and hit him smartly on the shins. Hubert began to cry and to try and kick his way to the door. But everything he kicked seemed to hit back. He kicked a building and a big block fell on his toe. He kicked at a Little-Builder office building and it fell over and clouted him on the back of the head. He kicked a book and it hit a lamp which fell and knocked a heavy wooden elephant off the bedpost onto Hubert's shoulder. He could hear the music of the circus parade growing fainter and fainter and so he bawled louder and louder.

Then he heard a tapping at his window. He crawled over and reached out. It was the rake with a note on it. He took the note and opened it. It said:

> *The only way you can get out of that trap*
> *is to put everything away where it belongs.*
> *If you hurry we will wait for you.*
>
> > Your friend,
> > Mrs. Piggle-Wiggle

Hubert began by finding the Little-Builder box. He took down an office building and put each piece in its right place. Then he put away the stone blocks, then the train tracks, the circus, the soldiers, the paints, the chemical set, the printing press, the books, the fire engines, the automobiles. He played little games, pretending that he was racing someone to see who could find the most parts of a game the quickest.

He had to take off the bedclothes and shake them in order to find the soldiers and the circus, and then he thought that as long as the bedclothes were off anyway, he

might as well make his bed. It was so lumpy when he finished he thought he had left some airplanes in it and took the covers off again and shook them. He made the bed again and this time it was neat and smooth. Hubert was proud.

He was under the desk finding the last piece of the Little-Builder when he heard the music again. He put the piece in the box, put the box in the closet, and tore down the stairs and out the front door.

There they came, Mrs. Piggle-Wiggle, all the children, and the CIRCUS! Hubert ran out to meet them and nobody said anything about the pan of orange paint stuck in his hair or the word XYPGUN printed on his cheek in purple ink.

Away they went down the street, Hubert carrying the flag and yelling the loudest.

The Fairies

by WILLIAM ALLINGHAM

illustrated by NINON

Up the airy mountain,
  Down the rushy glen,
We daren't go a-hunting
  For fear of little men;
Wee folk, good folk,
  Trooping all together;
Green jacket, red cap,
  And white owl's feather!

Down along the rocky shore
  Some make their home,
They live on crispy pancakes
  Of yellow tide-foam;
Some in the reeds
  Of the black mountain-lake,
With frogs for their watchdogs,
  All night awake.

High on the hilltop
    The old King sits;
He is now so old and gray
    He's nigh lost his wits.
With a bridge of white mist
    Columbkill he crosses
On his stately journeys
    From Slieveleague to Rosses;

Or going up with music
   On cold, starry nights,
To sup with the Queen
   Of the gay Northern Lights.

They stole little Bridget
    For seven years long;
When she came down again
    Her friends were all gone.
They took her lightly back,
    Between the night and morrow;
They thought that she was fast asleep,
    But she was dead with sorrow.
They have kept her ever since
    Deep within the lake,
On a bed of flag-leaves,
    Watching till she wake.

By the craggy hillside,
  Through the mosses bare,
They have planted thorn trees
  For pleasure here and there.
Is any man so daring
  As dig them up in spite,
He shall find their sharpest thorns
  In his bed at night.

Up the airy mountain,
   Down the rushy glen,
We daren't go a-hunting
   For fear of little men;
Wee folk, good folk,
   Trooping all together;
Green jacket, red cap,
   And white owl's feather!

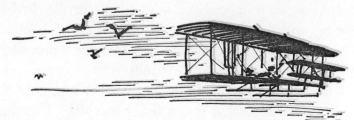

The Wright Brothers:

Pioneers of Flight

by ARCH WHITEHOUSE

illustrated by HARVEY WEISS

Bishop Milton Wright, of Dayton, Ohio, was a very jolly man, with a large and happy family—four boys and one little girl. Whenever he returned from an out-of-town trip his arms were always loaded with presents. It was a very exciting time, for no one could guess what the bishop would discover and buy for any of his children.

One day in 1878 he caused quite a commotion when he handed the two younger boys, Wilbur and Orville, a tricky little toy called a *hélicoptère*. It was made of bamboo, cork, and tissue paper, and it had two little propellers, which were whirled by rubber bands.

Neither of the boys had any idea what it was, until the bishop explained that it was a flying machine. They had never heard of such a thing, but when they wound up the propellers and turned it loose the little toy shot straight to the ceiling.

For about an hour the whole family sat in the living room and watched this marvelous plaything. Then the two boys decided it would be more fun flying it outdoors.

In a few minutes it was lodged in the top of a tree, and in trying to get it down they broke one of the propellers and tore some of the paper off the wings. They tried to repair it, but it would not fly again. Instead of begging their father to buy them another, they decided to make one themselves. A bigger one.

They experimented with larger wings and different kinds of propellers. They flew the results day after day in all sorts of weather and wondered if they could ever build a flying machine that would carry a man.

In those days it seemed that European experimenters were far ahead of America in the race to build an airplane. Otto Lilienthal, a German, and Stringfellow, an Englishman, had both built models that had flown. Then, too, it was a German by the name of Daimler who first perfected the automobile engine. What was more, the men who believed in balloons were putting Daimler's auto engine into their dirigibles and flying in any direction without the help of the wind.

Meanwhile the two Wright brothers were still experimenting with box kites and gliders. They were interested in all
kinds of tools. Neither went to college, because they felt
a high school education was enough for their kind of work.
They liked to be outdoors—and to make things. Once they
tried the printing business and even made their own press.

For a press bed they used an old discarded tombstone.

Eventually they designed a bicycle and began to manufacture it as a business. It was called the Van Cleve Cycle, named after their great-grandmother, one of the first settlers of their town.

One day Orville was in bed with typhoid fever. He was reading a Sunday newspaper and learned that Otto Lilienthal, the German scientist, had been killed while flying in a glider. Both he and his brother Wilbur were saddened by the news, but at the same time they were fascinated to learn that Lilienthal had flown for more than a quarter of a mile before the accident happened.

Immediately they took a renewed interest in flying. To catch up with what had been going on they wrote to the Smithsonian Institution and asked about books on the subject. The curator gave them a list, which included "Progress in Flying Machines," by the American experimenter Octave Chanute. They studied these books for months and constructed a glider kite and tried to work out some theories of their own.

All this took place in 1899.

Their first glider kite was about five feet wide and was flown in some fields outside Dayton. But they needed more wind to get the lift the kite required. When the Wrights wanted to know something they always went to the men who could give them the answers.

This time they called on the U. S. Weather Bureau. The head man there told them they might find what they wanted at a place called Kill Devil Hill which was near Kitty Hawk, North Carolina.

The Wrights had figured out that most glider accidents had happened because the experimenters had not been able to control the wing when the wind shifted. They had watched sea gulls and noted that they used a very simple control. When they tilted up to one side they simply pressed down the other wing tip until they were flying level again.

The Wrights figured that if they could make their glider kite's wing tips warp one way or the other they would not sideslip into the ground.

In October of 1900 they built and flew an eighteen-foot glider kite against a twenty-seven-mile-an-hour wind. Either Wilbur or Orville would lie on the bottom wing, while the kite was held by a light but strong rope.

Their wing-warping idea worked! They simply moved a stick back and forth whenever the kite tilted one way or the other. In the air they had absolute control, although some of their landings were very funny. After floating over a 100-foot sand dune for any length of time they would try to glide down to earth again. Usually they hit hard and the man on the wing would come rolling out head over heels, much to the amusement of the few loungers who watched these two crazy men trying to fly like the birds.

After that they worked out a rudder by which they could steer the kite, and then added a front elevator which enabled them to raise or lower their angle of flight. With these devices working properly they were able to make more dignified landings.

They went back to Kitty Hawk the next summer and made more than a thousand of these glider-kite flights. That winter they sat down and wrote out what they had discovered. When they checked their wing-curve figures and other findings with those of the well-known scientists, they realized the findings were quite different from the theories presented by the experts. They wondered if they had made some great mistake, but, since they had flown their glider so successfully, they decided to go ahead—no matter what the experts had said.

During the winter of 1901–02 they built a forty-foot biplane in the cellar of their bicycle shop. What money they had came from the sale of bicycles, which wasn't much. But they did most of the work themselves and lived as cheaply as possible. This time they decided to try to fly by engine power, and went all over the country looking for a secondhand automobile engine.

They didn't have much luck, but eventually they picked up enough parts of an old Pope-Toledo auto engine. Then they hired Charles E. Taylor, a local machinist, to help them convert it for use in an airplane. Taylor hadn't much idea of what they were doing, but he went to work and did as they told him.

After six weeks they had built their first Wright engine. They used four cylinders, hollowed out the crankshaft to make it lighter, and somehow figured out how to make an aluminum crankcase for the engine. It was nothing like the auto engines we know today.

This engine was bolted to the main spars of the bottom wing, and it was set up to run two propellers mounted between the wings. Two oversize bicycle chains connected the propellers with the engine, and they were all set.

When completed, the engine weighed 180 pounds and turned out about twelve horsepower. Today our 2600 h.p. engines weigh exactly 2600 pounds. The plane was all ready by the early fall of 1903, and on September 3 of that year it was crated and shipped to Kitty Hawk for its trial flight.

The Wright airplane would look very funny alongside any of the planes our pilots fly today. It was built of wood and wire and covered with bed sheeting stitched together on their sister Katherine's sewing machine.

While the Wrights had been experimenting and building their first biplane, another American was preparing to fly a giant monoplane down the Potomac River. It promised to be a thrilling race, as to who could get into the air first.

Dr. Samuel Pierpont Langley was a highly trained scientist. He was nationally known and for years had been working with considerable backing and publicity; whereas up to now the Wrights were unknown.

Dr. Langley was the secretary of the Smithsonian Institution. He had many influential friends, including President McKinley and Dr. Alexander Graham Bell. President McKinley had heard that certain Europeans were developing the Zeppelin for war purposes, so he induced the War Department to give Dr. Langley $50,000 to produce a man-carrying airplane.

Between October 7 and December 8, 1903, two attempts were made to fly Langley's plane from a launching rail mounted on a houseboat anchored in the Potomac. Neither attempt was successful. The official observers had to admit that Langley's entry had not flown—not even for a few feet. It was partially wrecked before it even cleared the take-off tracks.

The field was now wide open for the Wrights.

The two brothers tossed a coin to see who would make the first attempt. Wilbur won, and they dragged the biplane out and set it up on the launching rail. The older brother then took his place on the lower wing, lying flat beside the engine.

This was on December 14, just six days after Langley had failed for the second time.

There were no newspapermen on hand. Only five coast-guardmen from a nearby lifesaving station wandered in to give a hand. None of them thought much of this strange business, but at least it was a break in the monotony of patrolling a shore line beat.

There was little wind, and the Wrights decided to move the ship and its launching rail to the top of a sand dune about a quarter of a mile away. Wilbur probably was anxious on the first attempt; he nosed up too sharply. The biplane stalled and settled down in the sand. One skid was broken, but otherwise the Kitty Hawk biplane suffered no serious damage.

Then, three days later, December 17, 1903, they decided to try again—after repairing the damaged skid. It was a cold Thursday morning, and a gusty twenty-seven-mile-an-hour wind was blowing.

Wilbur said: "It's pretty risky, but we may as well try it. Go warm your hands by the fire first, Orville."

This time they had set up the launching rail near their little hangar. The only witnesses were three coastguardmen, a man named W. C. Brinkley, of Manseto, and a young boy from Nag's Head named Johnny Moore.

Wilbur set up a camera and stationed one of the coastguardmen behind it and told him to trip the shutter when the plane reached the end of the launching rail.

"Be careful now," he warned the guardman. "This may mean a lot to us if we get off."

This time Orville crawled on the lower wing and started the engine. He pulled a release wire and the biplane bravely nosed into the gale. It moved slowly at first, and Wilbur was able to run beside it for about forty feet.

Then gradually it rose off the rail and the coastguardmen
yelled: "She's off!" The Wright biplane stayed in the air
for 12 seconds and flew more than 120 feet—or approxi-
mately 31 miles an hour.

The great dream of man—to fly—had come true!

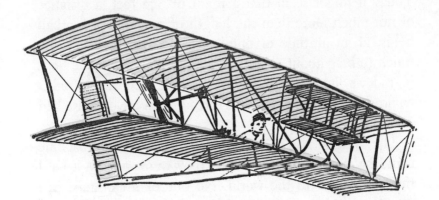

Then Wilbur tried again, and this time the biplane flew 195 feet in 13 seconds. Orville bettered this mark by 10 feet and stayed in the air for 15 seconds. At noon Wilbur made the record flight of the day, covering 852 feet and remaining in flight for 59 seconds!

Today it might seem that a flight of 852 feet, a distance of not much more than the length of a couple of football fields, at an altitude of only 12 to 14 feet, was nothing much to brag about. After all, we can make 500-mile hops in today's light planes. But it was the best the Wrights could do, and it was 852 feet further than anyone else had flown.

The Wrights had proved that a heavier-than-air machine could be built—and flown. But they were to have a hard time proving it to the world. No one of importance had seen the Kitty Hawk flights. The unbelievers were shown a few smudged photographs taken by a coastguardman. But no noted scientist or official observer had been present.

The scientific world was still lamenting Dr. Langley's failure. It was a great blow to their particular group. The announcement that two unknown bicycle mechanics had built a machine that had flown was hard to believe. To many people it was something of a joke.

After the Kitty Hawk flights the Wrights began to build a larger biplane. They used a field on a farm owned by Torrence Huffman at Sims Station, a short distance outside Dayton. They worked hard, and all through 1904 and 1905 they were making more than one hundred flights and by now had learned to turn, circle, and perform other simple maneuvers. The people in that area saw the plane almost every day and thought nothing of it; but officials in Washington still would not believe the Wrights could fly.

Because they were being ignored at home, the Wrights took their latest biplane to Europe. There they put on

some amazing exhibitions and won a new following. Their new plane was much improved and had seats for two, side-by-side. A French syndicate bought their European patent rights for $100,000, and for the first time the Wrights were enjoying official recognition and making some money out of their invention.

On September 21, 1908, Wilbur set a new world's record by flying fifty-two miles and remaining in the air for 1 hour, 31 minutes, 25 seconds. Later he astonished the world by carrying a passenger and then closed that triumphant year by flying seventy-seven miles in 2 hours, 20 minutes. That won him the French Michelin trophy and 20,000 francs, then worth $5,000.

By now the Wrights had the world at their feet. The world's greatest statesmen traveled hundreds of miles to see them fly, and royalty attended every exhibition.

Wilbur and Orville, with their sister Katherine, were guests of the British royal family at Windsor Castle; and the Royal Aeronautical Society awarded the brothers a gold medal for their many triumphs.

When they returned home their own state, Ohio, finally recognized their efforts. The governor conferred a medal. Next, President Taft received them at the White House and Congress pinned on another medal. But so far no one in America mentioned anything about their being "the first" to fly successfully a heavier-than-air machine. That most important recognition was not to come from aviation authorities in this country until many years later.

It was not until December 17, 1928, that official recognition of their life work was given. On that date, twenty-five years after their epochal flight, a small monument was erected at Kitty Hawk. A bronze plaque proclaimed: "The first successful flight of an airplane."

The Lovely Time

by AUDREY CHALMERS

illustrated by POLLY JACKSON

Maw was a cat.

As you may have guessed from her name, she was the mother of a great many kittens.

And as she lived with Mr. and Mrs. McCollum for twelve years, you might think that their neat brick house on Ontario Street was filled and surrounded with kittens and cats, small, medium, and big.

Not at all. As soon as Maw saw that her kittens were old enough to care for themselves, she settled them in nice homes of their own.

It is likely she first explained to them that when she was their age she had been left by her mother on Mr. McCollum's morning newspaper on the front steps, and look how well that had turned out.

Then, one by one, she took them for a walk—and came back by herself.

Mrs. McCollum got so she could tell when this was going to happen. "Maw has that look on her face today," she would tell Mr. McCollum at breakfast time.

Sure enough, that would be the day the kittens began to disappear.

At first Mrs. McCollum used to worry a lot over this.

"Now, Maw, you just show me where you have left those dear, little, helpless kittens," she would scold.

So Maw and Mrs. McCollum would go out walking together, and Maw would show Mrs. McCollum where she had left her kittens.

It might be two blocks away, or three, or six. But Maw always picked out a good home, usually one where there lived maiden ladies or children or lonely bachelors.

After a while Mrs. McCollum stopped worrying, and all went well until Sonny came along.

Sonny was the biggest and smartest in Maw's last family of six. He resembled his mother in looks, having a coat of shining black, a white bib under his chin, and four white socks.

He was so far ahead of his age that he was creeping out of the woodshed door before his brothers and sisters were able to leave their box.

More than once Maw had to carry him back from the

woodshed stoop where he was enjoying the look of the rain barrel, the white wash swinging from the clothesline, and the golden-glow hedge.

Also he started purring at an unusually early age, and he would do this whenever Mr. or Mrs. McCollum stopped to pat him.

They really hated to think of the time when this smart, beautiful, loving kitten would leave them.

But time and tide wait for no man. The day came when Mrs. McCollum could see that look on Maw's face, and one by one Sonny's brothers and sisters began to disappear.

Sonny was the last kitten that Maw took for a walk. She took him out one fine spring morning, and in the fine spring evening of the same day Sonny came back.

The next morning Maw took Sonny off again. This time she carried him by the fur on the back of his neck, although Sonny was really too big to be carried in this way.

She must have walked many blocks, because when she came back (by herself), she went right into her basket behind the kitchen stove and slept for a long time.

The next morning, bright and early, Sonny was back again.

This went on and on; no matter how nice a home Maw picked out for Sonny, Sonny always came back.

After a while Sonny grew too big and strong for Maw to take anywhere. That was when Maw began to look cantankerous, and act cantankerous, and sound cantankerous; in fact, she grew downright mean to Sonny.

She would not share her sleeping basket with him or her flowered bowl at mealtime, or the kitchen steps for washing up, or the golden patch of sunshine that lay on the front porch in the late afternoon. Neither would she share games of crouching and leaping through the fallen leaves, nor butterfly-chasing, nor tag, nor catching fireflies when it grew dark.

When Sonny tried to share in these things with his mother, she chased him away and all around the house. She chased him through the next-door neighbor's garden on the right and tripped up Mrs. Cattermole, who fainted and had to stay in bed for a week. She chased him through the open French window of the neighbor's house on the left, and scared the Misses Wilkins out of a year's growth. And every day, all summer long, she chased Sonny under the front porch.

Such unmotherly behavior on Maw's part made Mr. and Mrs. McCollum feel simply *terrible!*

Mr. McCollum had a talk with Sonny and told him he

was almost as big as his mother, so why in tarnation did he let her push him around? But it didn't seem to do any good.

Mrs. McCollum had a talk with Maw and told her it was a shame the way she treated her own son and tried to appeal to Maw's better nature. But it didn't seem to do any good.

Then Mr. McCollum tried to cheer up Mrs. McCollum by saying, "Well, one of these days we'll see what we will see."

He didn't know it, but—

That was the day!

It started out the same as any other day. By four o'clock Maw was settled on the front porch in the afternoon patch of sunshine, and on the way to a nap. And Sonny was settled in the damp wormy darkness under the porch. There was nothing unusual in this.

A break in the crisscross lattice allowed Sonny to put his head out and watch the butterflies hovering over the flower bed of Salvia and the moving shadows cast by the great tall trees on either side of the street. He always did this.

A long line of feet, marching two by two, now crossed Sonny's vision. The girls of Victoria Hall, on the corner of King and Ontario Streets, were on their way back from their afternoon walk. There was nothing unusual in this.

A jingle-jingle-jingle announced the passing of the Humpty Dumpty ice-cream man, on his way to the corner. In the spring, early summer, and fall, the Humpty Dumpty man carried on a brisk business in ice-cream cones and

Eskimo pies through the railings of the school gates.
Neither was this unusual.

Three minutes later the air was filled with angry shouts.
A Tutti-Frutti man and his dog, newcomers in town, had
taken possession of the Humpty Dumpty corner. Naturally this made the Humpty Dumpty man fighting mad.
Also, the Victoria Hall girls had managed to open the gates
and join in the fight. Soon the shouts were mingled with
clangs, bangs, whacks, thumps, bell-ringing, and barks.

This was *most* unusual, enough to wake up Maw and
bring her out into the middle of the road.

By this time the fight had reached its peak and was dying down, with Humpty Dumpty well ahead. The Tutti-Frutti dog looked around for fresh excitement. He caught sight of Maw halfway down the block. Being a stranger in town, he did not know that she was a tough customer—to him she was just another cat. And giving vent to a fine new outburst of barking, he sprang down the road toward her.

Taken by surprise, Maw lost her head and scrambled up the nearest tree. When the dog reached the tree, just three seconds too late, Maw was halfway up. And when he left to follow his master around the corner, she was three-quarters of the way up the tallest tree on the block—in fact, the tallest tree in town.

She turned herself around, head down, and took in the situation. "Mir-rr-aow! What a long way to the ground!" The strange moaning wail rose and fell, rose and fell, on the quiet evening air.

It sounded awful, but it was only a sample of what Maw could do.

By seven o'clock quite a few neighbors from up and down the block had joined Mr. and Mrs. McCollum at the foot of the tree. At seven-thirty Mr. McCollum was dragging a ladder from the back of the house. This was the time that Mr. McCollum liked to sit in the back yard and smoke his pipe. Instead he was placing the ladder against the tree and climbing up it. He stood on the top rung and told Maw that all she had to do was to come down to where he was and he would do the rest.

Maw did not believe him and backed farther up the tree. At eight-thirty a hopeful neighbor climbed the ladder

and held up a long pole. This pole had a noose on the end, cleverly baited with rare roast beef. All Maw had to do was come down five feet, walk into the noose, help herself to the rare roast beef, and the hopeful neighbor would do the rest.

Maw took one look at the noose, made a rapid retreat, reached a top branch, and gave out with a series of yowls that sent chills running up and down the spines of all within hearing distance.

The Misses Wilkins declared it put them in mind of banshees, storms at sea, ghosts, and graveyards.

Darkness fell and Maw could no longer be seen—only heard. Everyone went home to bed, but, alas, not to sleep —everyone, that is, except Sonny.

Afterward Mrs. McCollum remembered seeing Sonny appear suddenly from nowhere, stop by Maw's tree, and gaze upward. "If ever I saw a cat smile, I did then," she declared with feeling. This happened just as the town clock was striking the hour of nine.

The next time she saw Sonny, he was curled up in Maw's basket behind the kitchen stove and having the sleep of his life.

The morning dawned bright and clear. My, oh my, what a day! The sun sparkled and shone on dewy grass, golden-glow hedge, purple asters, Michaelmas daisies, and pink, white, and yellow button chrysanthemums.

The sun shone on Sonny taking a scoot through the raspberry bushes, chasing an orange-and-black butterfly,

chasing his tail, sharpening his claws on the stump of a tree, rolling in a patch of sandy earth, and crouching and leaping through the carpet of red and yellow leaves.

It shone on the kitchen steps, and on Sonny breakfasting from the flowered bowl, and on Sonny leisurely washing his face, white shirt front, and paws. It shone on Sonny having an altogether happy, lovely time and making the most of it.

And after the way of the sun that shines on the unjust along with the just, it shone on Maw in the treetop, nose down, tail up, and yowling.

The day was still young when Chief of Police Rooze and Constable Smith arrived on the scene, and only a half-hour older when the Hose and Ladder Company of the Fire Department drew up with a flourish in front of the McCollums' home. It was almost no older at all when the S.P.C.A. and about fifty friends and neighbors made their appearance.

Everyone went to work with a will to rescue Maw.

The firemen put up a twenty-foot ladder but failed to reach Maw by some ten feet.

They next hooked up the hose and brought it into play against Maw's location in the treetop. Maw expressed her opinion of this in a rising crescendo of yells, but held her position.

Then Agent Bowen of the S.P.C.A. took over. A smoky fire was started to windward of the tree. The crowd was assured that this would smoke Maw out. When it became plain that the crowd was about to be smoked out, but not Maw, Agent Bowen ordered the fire extinguished.

The S.P.C.A. had another idea. A wooden platform was hastily constructed and fitted to the top of the ladder. A beaver trap baited with catnip and salmon was placed on the platform. Onlookers were urged to be quiet and

all held their breath as they waited for Maw to enter the trap.

Maw stayed where she was.

At four o'clock Chief of Police Rooze and Constable Smith shook hands with Mr. and Mrs. McCollum and left. Everyone else followed suit.

From the front porch Sonny watched the departure of the Police Force and the Hose and Ladder Company and the S.P.C.A. and all the friends and neighbors. His position was a reclining one in the patch of afternoon sunshine. After a moment he changed it to a sitting one, and washed his shirt front, sides, and tail. He washed slowly and thoughtfully. Occasionally he paused to gaze upward —treetopward, to be exact. He kept on washing until he reached the last lap. Then he stood up, walked down the four porch steps, along the garden path, across the sidewalk, and over to the great, tall tree where Maw was.

Mr. McCollum was the first one to see it. "Laura, Laura!" he shouted. "Come quick! Something's happening!"

Mrs. McCollum came running. The yowling had stopped; in the electric silence Mr. McCollum pointed upward. Sonny was halfway up the tree, he was three-quarters up, he was all the way up! Sonny and Maw were touching noses.

"I'll bet my bottom dollar Sonny's telling Maw how to get down!" exclaimed Mr. McCollum.

"Of course he is! He's telling her to turn round and back down—the stupid old cantankerous thing!" Mrs. McCollum laughed affectionately.

113

There at the foot of the tree they held hands and watched. Again Sonny and Maw touched noses, and a third time, and a fourth. Then Sonny backed down, and Maw turned herself around and *backed down too!*

For an hour after her return to terra firma, home, and supper, Maw kept herself to herself on the kitchen steps. She looked as meek as Moses.

Then she arose, stretched, arranged her whiskers, held up her tail, and walked around the side of the house. There was still time before that patch of sunshine moved off the front porch.

Maw's timing proved to be correct. The golden patch was still there, but it was occupied. In the center, his gaze resting on a pot of ferns, lay Sonny.

Maw could hardly believe her eyes! But she pulled herself together, took up a crouching position, crept forward and—*Sszzzzztt!*

Nothing happened. Sonny's gaze, which missed Maw by about a foot, remained serenely on the pot of ferns.

Maw crept closer, out shot a paw, and, *smack!* she slapped Sonny on the side of the head. Again nothing happened.

This time Maw took a moment to recover—two or three moments in fact. She had only one trick left, and that was to spit. So she did. But the starch had gone out of Maw and it was a weak sort of spit, with none of the old get-up-and-go to it.

As for Sonny, he kept right on staring at the pot of ferns: only his tail began swishing in a half circle and his eyes grew darker—and larger.

Maw backed out of the sunshine to the side of the porch. There she sat with her back to Sonny, and looked up at a flock of crows passing overhead and down at the flower bed of Salvia. Somehow everything seemed different.

So she just sat, until she heard Sonny move—only a bit, a little bit to the right. Then she turned and walked back into the sunshine and lay down beside him.

The breeze stirred two pairs of whiskers, softly, gently. It was a pleasant feeling.

That's how they were when Mr. and Mrs. McCollum saw them through the porch window. "Maw and Sonny are sharing," said Mrs. McCollum happily. "Everything's going to be lovely now."

Dozens of small animals live on water lily leaves.

A Trip to the Pond

A pond is a new wonderland to learn about. In it are thousands of living things. Some may be as large as frogs and turtles. Others, which most people have never seen, are so small that a magnifying glass is needed to learn how amazing they are.

Nature lovers and young science students often catch many of these interesting animals and plants and bring them back alive. They use a small dip-net and a couple of glass preserve jars filled with water from the pond in which they go exploring. For a few days, at least, they can have a little fresh-water zoo to study.

Bullfrogs croak loudly.

The undersides of the floating leaves of water lilies found in ponds deserve a close look, because several dozen kinds of little creatures live there. In fact, they live on the stems and leaves of many different water plants.

The Bullfrog has about the deepest voice of all the frogs and a tame one will always "sing" when you make noise. When he is fully grown, his croaking makes you think of the bellowing of a bull. You may hear this amazing call any time from late spring until the end of summer. Believe it or not, he keeps his mouth closed while he makes this astonishing racket!

This giant-size frog takes several years to grow up. In the beginning he is only one of maybe twenty thousand little black eggs which his mother lays right in the water of the pond. But there is a record of one old grandfather Bullfrog who grew to weigh more than three pounds, and measured ten inches from the tip of his nose to the end of his body. His hind legs and feet were even longer than that!

Another of the large animals found in many ponds is the fat, strong Muskrat. He is a true rat, but his big hind feet have webs between the toes, somewhat like those of a duck. This makes him a very strong swimmer along the surface of the water, as well as underneath it. He can hold his breath for a long time, too.

Mr. Muskrat's usual food is pieces of plants. He often leaves the pond to feast on soft weeds and stems on shore, like the fellow in the photograph. But he also likes ripe apples and fresh-water clams, when he can find them. In winter he often eats the reed walls of his house!

Muskrats stay near water.

When summer comes, a great many ponds are covered with a queer bright green sheet. This is made up of trillions of tiny floating plants called Wolffias. They are the smallest flowering things in the world. In fact, they are so small that they are often called Water-meal.

Wolffia flowers are different from those of any other plant. Indeed, they are no more than little breaks on the upper sides of the leaves.

Duckweeds, too, are very small but common pond plants. They drift around in great masses on the surface of the water. The kind shown in the picture is called the Greater Duckweed. It has several small, waxy leaves which look somewhat like those of a dwarf clover. Around their edges there are a few flowers so small that you can hardly see them.

Short roots hang from the bottom of a Duckweed plant, but they never reach the bottom of the pond. A great scientist, looking through his powerful microscope, has discovered that these roots are covered with little creatures

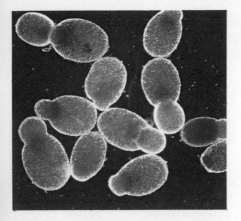

Wolffia's budding leaves

Duckweed's short roots

which find them a perfect place to live and eat.

Far below the Duckweeds there are likely to be small catfishes, often called Bullheads. Most fishes find their food by eyesight. But a Bullhead has a different idea. He can't see too well, down there at the bottom of the pond where there isn't much light. So, to help fill his stomach, he has queer-looking barbels, or "whiskers," which discover his food for him as he trails them along the muddy bottom.

In the same pond as the Bullheads there are silvery little fishes, commonly called "shiners" because of their color. They belong to the minnow tribe, and they usually swim well above the bottom, where there is plenty of light and clear water. Often large groups of them come to the surface and gobble great numbers of tiny insects.

Salamanders, which hatch from eggs laid in swampy

Catfish "see" with barbels.   Minnows are common in ponds.

ponds, live in the water until they are old enough to come out on damp, shaded land. While they are still in the water, they "breathe" through fringe-like gadgets known as "gills." These are able to gather oxygen from the water and so keep the little fellows alive. You can see one

Baby Salamander has gills.   A Snapping Turtle needs air.

Whirligig's air bubble

Two creeping Water Bugs

of these reddish gills sticking out of the neck of the Salamander in the picture. These peculiar animals eat many insects and other small water creatures.

The biggest of all pond animals is the Snapping Turtle. He grows quite slowly but often lives for many years. Finally he may weigh as much as fifty or even seventy pounds!

A Snapping Turtle is as bad-tempered as he is ugly. His hard, sharp-cutting jaws and long neck are perfect for catching and eating many kinds of other water creatures. Sometimes he even kills full-grown ducks. Mostly he stays on the pond's bottom. But he has to come up for a breath of air every now and then.

If you should ever come across a Snapping Turtle, be very careful. A fair-sized one can nip off your finger or toe as easily as you would slice an apple. And he does it

A Water Boatman swims rapidly with oarlike hind legs.

quick as a wink, too!

In every pond there are always plenty of bugs and beetles. There are groups of the shining black Whirligig Beetles zipping around on the surface of the water. When something scares them, they usually dive out of sight. At such times each of them carries a little bubble of air with him, so he can breathe under water. You can see this bubble in the picture. As soon as things quiet down, all the Whirligigs pop up again.

Creeping Water Bugs crawl about under water, but they too must take their air supply with them. And the Water Boatman, who uses his pair of long hind legs as if they were oars, carries his necessary air inside his wing covers. This air is what causes that silvery color which you see in his photograph.

Crayfish, which look somewhat like little lobsters, are found in many ponds. While they are small they hide under stones and dead plants on the bottom, so that other

123

Crayfish are scavengers.

creatures won't gobble them up. But when they get older they start wandering around, eating almost any tasty bit that they find in the mud.

A grown-up Crayfish uses his claws for self-defense as well as to pick up food. He can give you quite a pinch with them if he has to. But if an enemy should catch him by one leg, he will give a quick jerk, break off that leg at a particular spot, and dart away apparently unharmed!

Finally, there are always transparent masses of Snail eggs sticking to the stems of underwater plants and to stones on the bottom of the pond. They are tiny gadgets, but the baby Snails in them grow fast and soon develop shells of their own. Then the Snails go their way beneath the surface of the pond, where they eat the mossy green plants found on rocks.

Yes, ponds are wonderful places to learn about thousands of plants and animals. And during every season of the year the life and habits of these amazing creatures may be studied and enjoyed there.

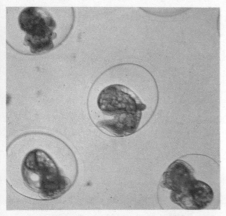
Snail eggs grow quickly.

124

Chief Dooley's Busy Day

by KAY *and* HARRY MACE

illustrated by RICHARD SCARRY

Chief Dooley walked down the main street of Newtown Center on his way to work.

"Good morning, Mrs. Hancock," he said to one of his old friends. "Nice day, isn't it?"

Just then a little boy came running up. "Hi, Chief," he called.

"Hello, Pinky," answered Chief Dooley. "You'd better hurry or you'll be late for school!"

All the way down the street, the Chief stopped and talked every few steps. He did this every morning, and how he did love it.

Chief Dooley was a policeman. He was the only policeman in this little town where everybody knew him, and of course, he knew everybody else who lived there.

It wasn't a very big town. There was just one main street with stores on both sides. There were lots of little side streets with houses and gardens.

Small as it was, the main street was always crowded in the morning. The grocery store, the bank, the post office, were all full of people. So, of course, you could find Chief Dooley right there every morning.

In the summer he wore a big, wide helmet, and you could see his pistol strapped right on his hip.

In the fall he wore a coat with shiny brass buttons, and a shiny police badge.

In the winter he wore a long, heavy overcoat and a cap with ear muffs.

And in the spring, when it rained, he wore a big, black slicker.

Every day, all year round, for just about as long as anyone could remember, Chief Dooley had been there to stop cars and trucks and buses so that people could cross the street. Sometimes he walked out into the street and held up his hand even if there was only one car coming. "I just naturally like to take care of everybody," he said.

He helped ladies with their big bags of groceries, and with their baby carriages. He mailed letters. He talked to the men about the news and fishing and the weather.

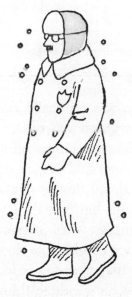

He was especially careful to be right on hand when kindergarten was over.

"Be sure you get off at the right corner," he said as he put Janet and Nancy on the bus.

A dozen times a day a driver might stop and ask, "Pardon me, but how do I get to Center Street?"

Finally, when everyone else had gone home, Chief Dooley checked the doors all along Main Street to make sure they were safely locked.

He did all these things every day.

Almost every day, something different happened, too!

There was the Monday when Susan came running up, all out of breath. She was almost crying.

"Chief Dooley, I've lost my new puppy. Have you seen him? Will you find him? Oh, please!" she gasped.

"There, there, Susie, of course we'll find your puppy." Chief Dooley took her by the hand. "Let's look down by the brook. That's where little dogs and little boys always go."

So Susie and Chief Dooley found Taffy down by the brook, barking at a chipmunk.

The next day, Tuesday, everybody heard the fire sirens. First, all the volunteer firemen jumped in their cars, and went off as fast as they could, while Chief Dooley held up all the rest of the traffic. Then he jumped in his car, too.

But it was just a grass fire up on Sunset Hill, and they had it out in no time at all.

Wednesday, somebody left an old truck parked at an angle on Main Street.

Chief Dooley made a note of the license number. He went into the grocery store, the drugstore, the bank, the newspaper store. Pretty soon, the owner came running out to move his truck.

Thursday, Tommy Bailey was climbing in his back yard. He slipped and went CRASH!

"Ow-wwwwwwww," he cried.

Tommy's daddy wasn't home, so whom did Tommy's mother call to take them to the hospital? Yes, of course, Chief Dooley.

Friday, Shirley Scott got married. Chief Dooley got one of the bride's very first kisses. Then he made sure that nobody followed the car when Shirley and her brand-new husband went driving off.

Chief Dooley always had a good time Saturday, at the Drum Corps parade. It wasn't work at all to make sure that nobody got in the way while the Drum Corps was marching and playing.

The pretty majorette waved, "Hi, Chief," as she twirled by.

On Sunday the people in Newtown Center went to church. So, of course, Chief Dooley was standing right in front of the church saying "Good morning" to everyone.

Yes, Chief Dooley liked being a policeman. He liked his town, and all the people in it. Only every once in a while, he wished that something really exciting would happen. "I wish I could show everyone how brave I am," he said.

Every night when he got home, he read in the paper about the exciting things that the policemen were doing in the big city not so very far away. All the policemen there seemed to be heroes.

DAILY PRESS
POLICE
HERO

Sometimes he read about a policeman who had saved the life of a little boy who had fallen in the river.

Sometimes he read about a policeman who had caught three men who had robbed a bank.

And sometimes he read about policemen who had been given medals for bravery by the Mayor. There were stories like this in the paper almost every night.

"I could do all those things if I were a city policeman," thought Chief Dooley. "Not much ever happens here. Newtown Center doesn't really need me. The people probably wouldn't even know I was gone."

Suddenly, one night, Chief Dooley came to a decision. "I'll ask the Mayor for a day off, and find out about a job as a city policeman. Then I can be a hero, too!"

The next morning, he asked the Mayor if he could take a trip to the city someday.

"Sure," said the Mayor, "why don't you go today? If anything comes up, I'll take care of it myself."

So Chief Dooley went to the city. He went straight to police headquarters, and he told the police chief all about the years that he had been a policeman in Newtown Center. "Now I'd like to be a policeman in the city," he said.

"We don't need any more men right now," said the Chief, "but I will be sure to let you know when we do. We need men like you here in the city."

"Thank you very much," said Chief Dooley as he said good-bye.

"I'll be a city policeman before very long," he thought. In a little while he was back in Newtown Center.

Right away, he knew there was something wrong.

'Way down at the station, he could hear the horns tooting. He looked up Main Street, and he started running. He ran as fast as he could. In just a minute he was in the middle of town.

Traffic was really in a snarl. Cars, trucks, buses, and even a bicycle or two, were all stopped. They were all honking their horns.

A truck was parked in front of the grocery store. The

bus was stalled. Someone was even fixing a flat tire right on Main Street.

Chief Dooley blew his whistle.

"Come on, there," he shouted, waving his hand. It took him almost half an hour to get the traffic all straightened out.

Just as the last few cars went by, Mrs. Bugbee came run-

ning. "I can't find Jimmy! I've looked everywhere! Have you seen him?" she gasped.

"No, but I'll start looking right away," Chief Dooley told her as he headed for the brook.

Before he had gone two steps, the Mayor came running, too.

"Gosh, Chief," he said, "am I glad you're back! Things are in a terrible state! We had a fire in Fred Dilly's garage, and the hose truck almost didn't get through, there were so many cars in the way. I tried to help, but I got knocked down, and Ben Staley's fender got bumped, and——"

"I'm sorry, Mayor," Chief Dooley began, "I——"

"Chief Dooley, Chief Dooley!" cried Mrs. Walker. "I've

138

lost my purse!"

"Oh, dear!" said Chief Dooley. "Now just a minute everybody. Be patient for a little while. I'll fix everything."

And of course he did.

He was really tired by the time he got home. It had been a busy day. He propped his feet up on the table, and began to read the paper. All of a sudden, he wasn't tired at all.

There on the front page of the paper was a picture. *His* picture.

There was a story, too, all about Chief Dooley. He read about how he had just set a record for the whole state.

In twenty-five years, nobody had ever been badly hurt as long as he was on duty.

He read about some of the funny things that had happened to him, and about some of the not-so-funny things.

Tomorrow there was going to be a parade. The Mayor was going to make a speech. The Drum Corps was going to play. And what was this? He, Chief Dooley, was going to get a medal!

"Whew!" said Chief Dooley. "What a day this has been!" Suddenly he remembered how the day began, and he felt very ashamed that he had ever even thought about leaving Newtown Center. "Why," he said, "I don't have to get a medal, or have my picture in the paper. I couldn't possibly leave. I belong here."

And he went happily off to bed to dream about tomorrow.

Tell Me About People

by ELLEN WALES WALPOLE

illustrated by THERESA SHERMAN

Text from *Children Ask*, copyright, 1947, by Ellen Wales Walpole, and published by Barnes & Noble, Inc.

140

HOW MANY PEOPLE ARE THERE
IN THE WORLD?

There are more than 3,000 million people living in the world today. That is over three thousand millions. This is more people than ever lived in the world before.

Almost two hundred million of these people live in the United States. This may seem a great number of people. But less than one tenth of the people in the world live in the United States.

The country with the greatest number of people is China. There are almost seven hundred million people in China. There are almost four times as many people in China as there are in the United States.

Why are there more people in the world now than ever before? One reason is that we know more about health. More babies live to grow up now than in the past. More of the older people who become ill get well and live longer. Life is better than it was.

WHAT IS HISTORY?

History is the story of men.

We do not know much about the very early people who lived on earth. They were not able to write. So they did not leave us the story of their doings.

When men learned to write, they kept records of the things they did. They wrote of their great kings and their own brave deeds. They wrote about their battles. They wrote about the journeys they made and the things they discovered.

This is history—the story of people.

Some of these old stories were written on a sort of paper. We have found many old papers in the deserts of Egypt. There they were kept dry and safe for thousands of years.

We can read them and tell what men were doing thousands of years ago.

Some of the old stories were carved on rocks and stones. We have found some carved stones that tell what the Indians in Mexico were doing hundreds of years ago. The tales of kings who lived thousands of years ago were found in Asia.

IS IT BETTER TO BE A MAN OR A WOMAN?

Half the people in the world are men and half are women.

There are some things that men do better than women. They are usually stronger than women. They can lift more and do the heavy work. But this does not make them better than women.

There are some things in the world that women do better than men. They are usually better at looking after a home than men are. They are able to take care of children better. But this does not make them better than men.

Women seem to be more interested in clothes than men are. Men seem to be more interested in sports than women are. But this does not make one more important than the other.

Men are just as important as women, and women are just as important as men. When you grow up, you will marry a man if you are a girl, a woman if you are a boy. You will share life together.

WHAT IS A RELATIVE?

A relative is someone in your own family. Your closest relatives are your mother and your father. Your brothers and sisters are also your close relatives.

Your grandmothers and your grandfathers are your relatives. So are your aunts and uncles and cousins.

Some people even say their second cousins are relatives. These are the children of their cousins. If you went on finding second cousins and third cousins, you would learn that you had a great many relatives.

You might say that all the people who had married these relatives of yours are also relatives of one another. You might say that the relatives of these people are also your relatives.

If you went on far enough, you would find a very strange thing. You would find that you are related to every other person in the world.

And in a way you would be right.

WHY DO PEOPLE DO DIFFERENT WORK?

What is your favorite game? What do you like to do best in the world? Do you like to play ball? Build blocks? Play hopscotch? Skate?

Whatever your favorite game may be, you will most probably play it best. If you like to build blocks, you will be most likely to do it well.

Whenever you get the chance, you do what you like best to do. So you get much practice. You think a great deal about things you like best to do and so you learn much about such things.

Grownups, too, have things they like to do. Some like to build. They become builders and engineers. Some like to draw pictures. They become painters and artists.

In the past, people did not choose the kind of work they liked to do. Often they hated their work. Now more and more people choose for their work the thing they like best to do.

What will you choose?

The best way to have fun is to share it with someone. The best games you play you play with someone. You certainly could not have fun by yourself for very long.

The people we share our things with are our friends.

Most people have one dearest friend. They share their toys, their books, and even their secrets. Sometimes this friend is a brother or a sister. More often it is someone outside the family. It is mostly someone about the same age.

Most people have a group of friends as well as one special friend.

Real friends are very fond of each other. They never do anything to hurt each other if they can help it. When they do, they forgive each other.

We have friends to share our fun and good times.

Think how dull it would be to go on a picnic all by yourself!

146

DO ALL PEOPLE EAT THE SAME KIND OF FOOD?

Most of the people in the world eat the same kind of food. They eat meat, fruit, vegetables, cheese, and cereals.

In America our meat is mostly beef, pork, or lamb. This is because cattle, pigs, and sheep do well here. People in some lands eat deer. Some people in Africa even catch and eat an elephant once in a while.

We eat wheat and corn because those cereals grow well in our country. People in India eat rice and millets because those cereals grow well in their country. People in China eat a great deal of rice.

Most of our milk comes from cows, but in some places people use milk from goats or even reindeer.

As the people of the world mix together more and more, they learn to like each other's food. Bananas do not grow well in America, but we have learned to like them.

WHY DO PEOPLE SPEAK DIFFERENT LANGUAGES?

There have never been so many people in the world as there are now. In the past, men lived in little groups here and there. Some of these people lived in little groups shut off from the rest of the world for thousands of years.

They did not talk with the people who lived in other parts of the world. Often they didn't even know about them.

These little groups of people spoke their own languages.

They made up new words and they forgot old ones. After a time they had a language that no one but themselves could understand.

Today little groups of people can no longer live by themselves shut off from the rest of the world. Airplanes, fast ships, radio, and television have joined all the people together.

For the first time men everywhere want to get together and understand each other. As men have always done wonderful things if they tried hard enough, some day they will do this, too.

WHY DO PEOPLE OF OTHER LANDS WEAR STRANGE CLOTHES?

They don't. What may seem strange to you may seem very ordinary to an Arab. In fact, he may think your clothes a little strange.

People are giving up the idea that it is foolish for others to wear clothes which are different from their own. We are learning that some clothes which are different from our own are very beautiful indeed.

Have you ever seen a beautiful coat all covered with flowers done with needlework that came from China? Have you ever seen a lovely lace shawl that came from Spain? Didn't you want to try them on?

Haven't you ever wanted to dress up in Indian clothes?

It would be a very dull world if all the people were dressed alike. Some of the strange clothes worn by people of other lands are very interesting.

WHY AREN'T ALL HOUSES ALIKE?

People need houses to protect themselves from the weather. There are all sorts of ways of protecting us from the weather, and there are all sorts of houses.

Campers in the woods like the shelter of a tent. Indians and Arabs like to live in tents because they can pack them up and move away when they want to.

People in very hot lands make light houses or huts of

reeds and rushes. They make their houses from things that grow nearby.

Some Eskimos make winter houses from frozen snow. They have no reeds and rushes. Frozen snow is the only thing they have that is strong enough to stand against the winter storms.

We have different kinds of houses. We have frame or wooden houses in which families live. We have great buildings with separate apartments in which many families live.

WHAT IS A GOVERNMENT?

Has your mother ever settled a quarrel between you and your brother or sister? Perhaps you both wanted the same apple and your mother showed you how you could divide it fairly.

Even in very early times, when men lived together in small groups, they needed someone to see that they were fair to each other. They needed someone to show them how to divide their lands fairly, or how to divide the work fairly.

This was the beginning of government.

Later men had kings to help them act fairly. But often the kings themselves were not fair.

In our own day we have a government to help us be fair to each other. The government makes plans and laws to see that no one is unfair to the rest.

If we do not think our government is fair to everyone, we can change it.

151

WHY IS IT WRONG TO TAKE
OTHER PEOPLE'S THINGS?

Suppose you had a little puppy that you loved very much. Suppose you had fed it and cared for it a long time. Maybe you had taught it some tricks. You loved it very much. And it loved you very much. It was your very own puppy.

Then suppose one day a friend came to play with you. Suppose he said, "I like the puppy, too. I want it. I am bigger than you and I am going to take it away with me."

Or suppose a younger friend said, "I want the puppy,

too. I am going to have it because I am only a baby."

You would say, "That's not fair!" and you would be right.

We do not take things that belong to other people because it is not fair.

Even if people don't seem to care much about their things, it is unfair to take them. Just to make sure, always ask whenever you want something that is not yours.

WHY DO WE HAVE TO HELP PEOPLE?

Do you remember when you were a baby? Well, when you were, there were many things you could not do for yourself. There were times when you had to be helped. You may not remember it, but there was even a time when you had to be fed.

Did you ever help a child younger than yourself? Maybe you helped to feed a baby. Maybe you helped a little child to learn something. Maybe you told him something he wanted to know.

All that is helping others.

Everyone in the world needs help at some time or other. Young babies, old people, and sick people all need our help.

Most people are glad to help others. It makes them feel useful. Perhaps you feel that way when you help others.

The more you learn to help other people, the more grown-up you become.

WHY ARE NEW INVENTIONS MADE?

A boy was told to scare the birds away from a patch of strawberries. He wanted to play instead. So he made a scarecrow and let it do his work for him.

That was an invention.

A boy had to water a garden every day. He grew tired of carrying water from the stream. So he dug a deep furrow and let the water run in by itself.

That was an invention.

Most inventions are made to do people's work for them. Some are made just to give us more fun. Think of all the trips a telephone saves. Think of all the work a washing machine saves.

Think of all the fun we get from the movies or television. Think what a wonderful invention a clock is.

Take a look around your house. Find all the inventions that make life easier and happier for your family.

DO PEOPLE KNOW MORE
THAN THEY USED TO?

Every year people discover many new things. They discover new inventions, new machines for making life easier and more pleasant.

All this is very good. It helps us to enjoy more things.

But to enjoy these new inventions we have to learn how to use them. We have to learn how to drive cars and planes. We have to learn how to find any channel we want on television. We have to know how to work our electric trains.

In days gone by, people did not know any of these things because the inventions had not been made.

Every year we have to learn to use a few more things. We shall have to go on doing this all our lives if we want to keep up with the new and better ways of living.

The best way to be on the safe side is to make sure you know all about reading and arithmetic. Then you can figure new things out for yourself at all times.

Let's Go to Greece

At the southern tip of the Balkan Peninsula in Europe lies the small country called Greece. Greece has a long coastline on the Aegean, Ionian, and Mediterranean Seas. In these waters there are many beautiful Greek islands like sunny Rhodes, Mykonos, lovely Corfu, and Crete.

Through the centuries Greece was invaded by foreign conquerors and shaken by earthquakes. Because so much of her land is mountainous, farming has always been difficult and most of the people poor. Yet, in spite of these hardships, Greece has had a proud history and heritage. When the rest of Europe was uncivilized, Greece was the greatest nation in the world! For over a thousand years Athens, her capital, was the cultural center of the Western world. Even today the West owes its basic ideas of democracy, philosophy, drama, art, and architecture, to Greece.

The Greeks are a hardy, industrious, and sociable people. They spend their days outdoors in the sunshine, tending their small farms, and coaxing wheat, barley, corn, currants, olives, and grapes from the dry soil. They raise sheep and goats, weave their own cloth, fish in the seas about them, and amuse themselves with music and dancing.

Since 1821, Greece has been an independent nation with a constitutional monarchy. Her king, like England's, is largely symbolic. With America's aid, Greece is now overcoming her farming problems, building up her industries, and welcoming visitors who come to see the Acropolis and other great monuments from her glorious past.

The Flag of Greece

Long ago the island of Corfu was a great seafaring power

The Parthenon was built for the Goddess Athena in 438 B.C. It stands on the Acropolis outside Athens.

MEDITERRANEAN

IONIA

OLYMPIA

PELOPONNESUS

PATR

KALAMATA

GYTHEION

6

SPARTA

ARCADIA

TRIPOLIS

ARGOS

CORINTH

13

1

CANEA

C R E T E

PIRAEUS

ATHENS

THE

7

CANDIA

CNOSSUS

9

C Y C L A D E S

S E A

MYKONOS

4

I S L A N D S

12

CHIOS

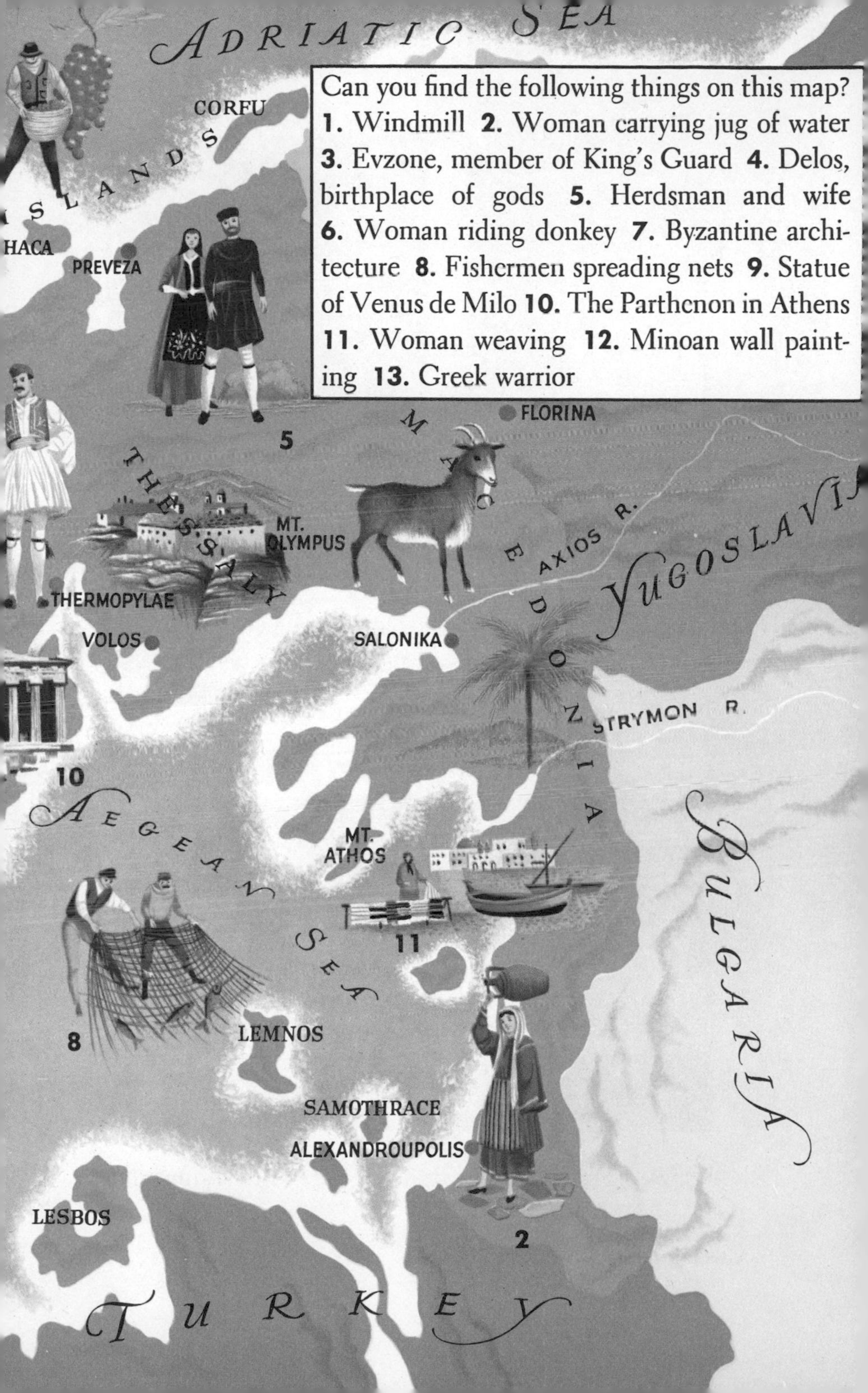

ADRIATIC SEA

CORFU

ISLANDS

HACA

PREVEZA

Can you find the following things on this map?
1. Windmill **2.** Woman carrying jug of water
3. Evzone, member of King's Guard **4.** Delos,
birthplace of gods **5.** Herdsman and wife
6. Woman riding donkey **7.** Byzantine architecture **8.** Fishermen spreading nets **9.** Statue
of Venus de Milo **10.** The Parthenon in Athens
11. Woman weaving **12.** Minoan wall painting **13.** Greek warrior

5

FLORINA

THESSALY

MT. OLYMPUS

MACEDONIA

AXIOS R.

YUGOSLAVIA

THERMOPYLAE

VOLOS

SALONIKA

STRYMON R.

BULGARIA

10

AEGEAN SEA

MT. ATHOS

11

8

LEMNOS

SAMOTHRACE

ALEXANDROUPOLIS

2

LESBOS

TURKEY

Left, Mykonos is a typical seacoast town with windmills, tiny streets, small white houses, and chapels.
Right, Priests of the Greek Orthodox Church are leaders in civic as well as religious matters.

Rhodes once protected Christianity from Turkish invaders.